What a Wonderful, Wonderful School

ISBN 10-digit: 1-59318-858-7

ISBN 13-digit: 978-1-59318-858-0

12 11 10 09 08 07   2 3 4 5 6

Printed in the United States of America

Published and Distributed by

Sopris West™
EDUCATIONAL SERVICES

A Cambium Learning Company

4093 Specialty Place • Longmont, CO 80504 • (303) 651-2829
www.sopriswest.com

JDE 148902

TABLE OF CONTENTS

CHICKA CHICKA BOOM BOOM cover courtesy of Aladdin/Simon & Schuster.
Cover by Eric Carle from BROWN BEAR, BROWN BEAR, WHAT DO YOU SEE?
Text by Bill Martin, Jr., Illustration ©1992 by Eric Carle. Reprinted by permission
of Henry Holt and Company, LLC. THE LISTENING WALK cover courtesy of
HarperCollins Children's Books.

Units 1, 2, and 3
ILLUSTRATION CREDITS
Lap Book illustrations: Philip A. Weber Jr.

What a Wonderful, Wonderful School

Lap Book 1

UNITS 1 • 2 • 3

READ WELL®

Sopris West Educational Services

What a Wonderful, Wonderful School

Join Mrs. B and her class of little ants for a warm and hearty welcome to a new school year. Sing songs, do art projects, and play games.

Chicka Chicka Boom Boom

by Bill Martin Jr and John Archambault
illustrated by Lois Ehlert

Related Literature

Bill Martin Jr / Eric Carle

Brown Bear, Brown Bear, What Do You See?

Related Literature

UNIT 3 • **What Do You Hear?**

Fiction • Rhyming Narrative: by Mrs. B, illustrated by Philip A. Weber Jr.

Summary: Mrs. B and her class take their first field trip to a farm. They have fun listening to barnyard sounds, playing rhyming games, and having a picnic.

Special Interactive Reading Activity: Students join in with the little ants as they make barnyard rhymes and play barnyard rhyming games.

Related Follow-Up Activity: Bookmaking

Related Literature

Hello

What a Wonderful, Wonderful Class

What a Wonderful, Wonderful Class

INTRODUCTION

The title of your new story is "What a Wonderful, Wonderful Class."
Everyone, what's the title of the story? (What a Wonderful, Wonderful Class)
This story is about a class just like ours.
Look at the picture. Everyone, who goes to this school? (ants)

What a Wonderful, Wonderful Class

by Mrs. B

illustrated by Philip A. Weber Jr.

Chapter 1

Welcome

In the anthill, the ants were busy—taking care of the baby ants, building new rooms, storing food, and meeting with the queen.

Everyone, let's look at some of the rooms and talk about what the ants are doing.

In Ant School, there was great excitement.

It was the first day of school for the littlest ants.

Mrs. B gathered all her new students around her.

The little ants waited quietly. (They were a little scared.)

Then Mrs. B smiled and gently said, "Welcome! Welcome to Ant School. It is a wonderful, wonderful school."

Mrs. B pushed up her glasses and said, "I am SO GLAD you are here."

Everyone, who is the story about? (Mrs. B and her students)

The little ants smiled back. Everyone in Mrs. B's class was smiling.

Everyone, show me a smile.

Mrs. B said, "This is going to be a wonderful year. I can see I have a wonderful, wonderful class."

Mrs. B said, "Today you are going to meet two of the special ants who work here. They are my friends, and they will be your friends too!" Then Mrs. B said, "I'm going to read you a story about these two special ants."

Everyone, who is Mrs. B going to read about? (two special ants)

Mrs. B read, "This very special ant loves to read. He reads stories to children."

What does the first special ant love to do? (He loves to read stories to children.)

Mrs. B read, "This very special ant helps little ants (like you) find books to read. He works in a room with hundreds and hundreds of books."

Where does he work? In a room with . . . (hundreds and hundreds of books).

Mrs. B continued reading, "This special ant is the librarian." Then Mrs. B said, "We will visit the librarian a little later." All the little ants clapped their hands.

Everyone, clap your hands.

Mrs. B said, "Now I'm going to read about another very special ant who works in our wonderful, wonderful school. She likes our school to look great."

What do you know about the second special ant? She likes the school to look . . . (great).

This special ant
works in the library,
in all the classrooms,
in the restrooms,
in the hallway,
even in the cafeteria.

Mrs. B read, "This special ant works in the library, in all of the classrooms, in the restrooms, in the hallway, even in the cafeteria. She works all over the school.

Where does she work? She works . . . (all over the school).

"She has many tools. She repairs things for us. She helps keep our school clean."

What else does this ant do? (She has tools. She repairs things. She keeps the school clean.)
Raise your hand if you think you know who this very special ant is.

Mrs. B continued reading, "This special ant is the custodian."
Then Mrs. B said, "We will visit the custodian a little later."
All the little ants clapped their hands.

Everyone, clap your hands.
We have a librarian and a custodian in our school too.
They are special people in our school.

END OF CHAPTER 1

See the unit teacher's guide for the related activity: Tour 1 • Special People.

What a Wonderful, Wonderful Class

CHAPTER 2 INTRODUCTION

In Chapter 1 of "What a Wonderful, Wonderful Class,"
you met Mrs. B and her students.
Everyone, who is the story about? (Mrs. B and her students)
Today, we're going to read more about Mrs. B's class.

Chapter 2

Getting Acquainted

Mrs. B said, "Today you are going to meet two more special ants who work at our school. They are my friends, and they will be your friends too."

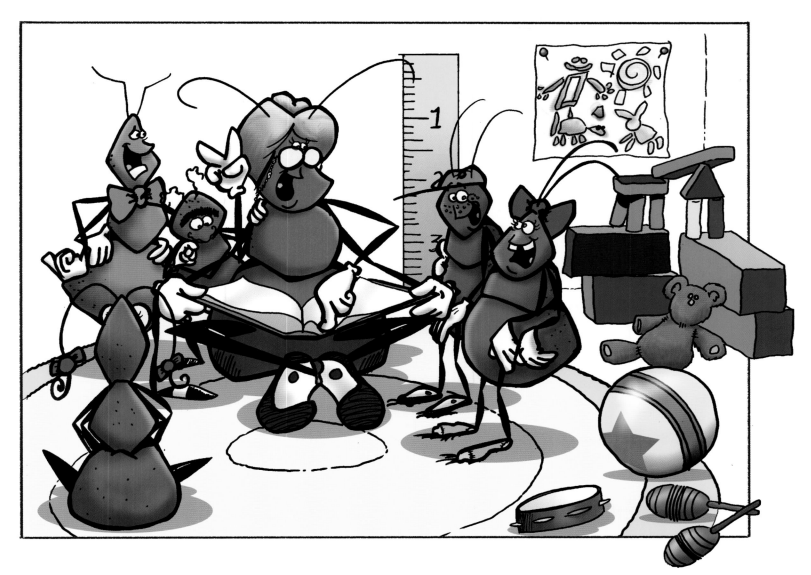

Then Mrs. B said, "I'm going to read a story about these two special ants."

Who is Mrs. B going to read about? (two more special ants who work at Ant School)

Mrs. B read, "This first special ant loves to read to children too. She works all over our school—just like the custodian."

"This special ant works with the little ants in the school.

Everyone, who does she work with? (the little ants)

She also works with the adult ants in the school.

Everyone, who else does she work with? (the adult ants)

She even works with the ant families.

Wow! She even works with the . . . (ant families).

This very special ant is in charge of our wonderful, wonderful school."

Mrs. B continued reading, "This very special ant is the principal."

Then Mrs. B said, "We will visit the principal a little later."

All the little ants clapped their hands.

Everyone, clap your hands.

Mrs. B said, "Now I am going to read about another special ant in our wonderful, wonderful school. This special ant also works with the little ants, the adult ants, and the ant families."

Mrs. B read, "This very special ant works in the office. She works on a computer and answers the phone."

What does this special ant do? She works in the . . . (office). She works on a . . . (computer). She answers the . . . (phone).

Mrs. B continued reading, "This very special ant is the secretary."

Then Mrs. B said, "We will visit the secretary a little later."
All the little ants clapped their hands.

Everyone, clap your hands.

Mrs. B put down her book. She said, "Our wonderful, wonderful school has many special ants. But you are the most important ants of all!"

Then Mrs. B said, "Stand up if you are a special ant in this school."

All the little ants stood up.

"That's right!" said Mrs. B. "Each and every one of you is a special ant. That is why this is such a wonderful, wonderful school."

Everyone, stand up. You are special people in our school.

Everyone, who are you? (special people) That is why this is such a wonderful, wonderful school too!

END OF STORY

See the unit teacher's guide for the related activity: Tour 2 • Special People.

What Do You See?

Mrs. B's Guessing Games

Mrs. B's Guessing Games

PREPARATION
Before reading, pass out student binoculars and have students dramatize the story.
If you haven't made the binoculars, have students use their hands.

INTRODUCTION
This is another story about Mrs. B and her wonderful, wonderful class.
The title of the story is "Mrs. B's Guessing Games."
Everyone, what is the title? (Mrs. B's Guessing Games)
You'll enjoy hearing about the games the little ants play with their binoculars.

Mrs. B's
Guessing Games

by Mrs. B

illustrated by Philip A. Weber Jr.

Chapter 1

What Do You See?

Every day at school, Mrs. B had something fun for the little ants to do. One day, she passed out binoculars to all her students. Mrs. B said, "Today we get to play a guessing game. This game is called *Little Ants, Little Ants, What Do You See?*"

Mrs. B said, "Everyone, say the name of the game." All the little ants said, "Little Ants, Little Ants, What Do You See?"

Mrs. B said, "Little ants, we are going on a tour of Ant School."
All the little ants clapped their hands.

Everyone, clap your hands.

Mrs. B's students lined up in two rows at the door. Then
two by two, the little ants walked down the hall.

Soon the little ants walked into another room. Mrs. B asked,
"Little ants, little ants, what do you see?"

Everyone, what did Mrs. B ask? (Little ants, little ants, what do you see?)

The little ants held up their binoculars.

Everyone, look through your binoculars at the book.
What do you see? (ants reading at a table, a clock on the wall . . .)
Everyone, please put your binoculars down.

Mrs. B said again, "Little ants, little ants, what do you see?"
Anthony raised his hand.

"What do you see, Anthony?" asked Mrs. B.

Anthony said, "I see hundreds and hundreds of books."

Everyone, look through your binoculars at the page.
What do you see? (hundreds and hundreds of books)
Everyone, please put down your binoculars.

Mrs. B said, "Yes, there are hundreds and hundreds of books, so we must be in the . . . "

"Library!" said all the little ants.

Mrs. B said, "Oh, you are such smart little ants. You are right! We are in the library."

Two by two, the little ants left the library. They walked down the hall and through a big door. Mrs. B asked, "Little ants, little ants, what do you see?"

Annie raised her hand. Mrs. B asked, "What do you see, Annie?"

Annie said, "I see little ants playing on the big toy."

Andrew raised his hand.

"What do you see, Andrew?" asked Mrs. B.

Andrew said, "I see little ants playing hopscotch."

Everyone, look through your binoculars at the book.

What do you see? (little ants playing hopscotch, playing on the big toy . . .)

Put your binoculars down.

Mrs. B said, "Yes, there are little ants playing on the big toy. There are little ants playing hopscotch. So we must be on the . . . "

"Playground!" said the little ants.

Mrs. B said, "Oh, you are such smart little ants. You are right! We are on the playground."

Everyone, where are the ants? (on the playground)

Mrs. B said,
"We've had such
a fine time today.
Let's go play on
the playground for
awhile."

In this chapter, Mrs. B and her class played a game called *Little Ants, Little Ants, What . . .* (Do You See?).

In the library, they could see . . . (hundreds and hundreds of books).

On the playground, they could see . . . (little ants playing on the big toy, little ants playing hopscotch).

END OF CHAPTER 1

See the unit teacher's guide for the related activity: Tour 1 • Special Places.

Mrs. B's Guessing Games

CHAPTER 2 INTRODUCTION

In Chapter 1, Mrs. B and the ants played a game.
Everyone, do you remember the name of the game?
(Little Ants, Little Ants, What Do You See?)

In Chapter 2, Mrs. B and the little ants will play a
new game.

Chapter 2

Where Might We Be?

The next day, Mrs. B gathered all the little ants around her.

She said, "Yesterday we played *Little Ants, Little Ants, What Do You See?*"

"Today we are going to play a different game," said Mrs. B.

All the little ants clapped their hands.

Everyone, clap your hands.

"We're going to play *Little Ants, Little Ants, Where Might We Be?*"

Everyone, what are they going to play? (Little Ants, Little Ants, Where Might We Be?)

All the little ants clapped again. Then Mrs. B passed out the binoculars.

Mrs. B's students lined up in two rows at the door. Then two by two, the little ants walked down the hall.

Soon the little ants walked into a room. Mrs. B asked, "Little ants, little ants, what do you see?" The little ants held up their binoculars.

Eaton raised his hand. "What do you see, Eaton?" asked Mrs. B.

Eaton said, "I see one grown-up ant talking on the phone."

Everyone, hold up your binoculars and look at the book.

What do you see? (one grown-up ant talking on the phone)

Put your binoculars down.

Mrs. B asked again, "Little ants, little ants, what do you see?"

Eli raised his hand. "What else do you see, Eli?" asked Mrs. B.

Eli said, "I see another grown-up ant helping a daddy ant."

Where do you think the ants might be?

Mrs. B asked, "Little ants, little ants, where might we be?"

All the little ants said, "In the office!"

Mrs. B said, "Oh, you are such smart little ants. You are right! We are in the office."

Everyone, where are the ants? (in the office)
Nod your head if you were right.

Two by two, the little ants continued walking down the hall until they came to a very big room.

Everyone, where are the ants? (in a very big room)
Did they go outside? No, they are in a . . . (room).

Mrs. B asked, "Little ants, little ants, what do you see?"

The little ants held up their binoculars.

Hernando raised his hand.

"What do you see, Hernando?" asked Mrs. B.

Hernando said, "I see little ants playing with balls."

Everyone, hold up your binoculars and look at the page.

Where do you think the ants might be? (in a very big room, in the gym . . .)

Put your binoculars down.

Edith raised her hand.

"What do you see, Edith?" asked Mrs. B.

Edith said, "I see little ants jumping rope."

Everyone, hold up your binoculars and look at the page.
The ants are in a big room. Some ants are playing with balls, and some ants are jumping rope.
Put your binoculars down. Now where do you think the ants might be?

Mrs. B asked, "Little ants, little ants, where might we be?"

All the little ants said, "In the gym!"

Mrs. B said, "Oh, you are such smart little ants. You are right! We are in the gym."

Nod your head if you were right.

Mrs. B said, "We've had such a fine time today.
Let's play awhile."

In Chapter 2, Mrs. B and the little ants played a game called *Little Ants, Little Ants, Where Might We Be?*

Where were they when they saw one grown-up ant talking on the phone? (in the office)

Where were they when they saw little ants jumping rope? (in the gym)

Mrs. B and her class had fun playing their games.

END OF STORY

See the unit teacher's guide for related activities: Tour 2 • Special Places; Bookmaking.

What Do You Hear?

The Field Trip

The Field Trip

INTRODUCTION

Mrs. B's class has had a great time.

They've met special people, and they've played guessing games.

The title of this story is "The Field Trip."

Everyone, what is the title of the story? (The Field Trip)

In this story, Mrs. B and the little ants go on a field trip. A class goes on a field trip when their teacher travels with them away from school to learn new things.

Everyone, what are Mrs. B and the little ants going on? (a field trip)

The Field Trip

by Mrs. B

illustrated by Philip A. Weber Jr.

Chapter 1
Barnyard Sounds

Where do you think Mrs. B and the little ants are going on their field trip?

Mrs. B's class lined up at the entrance of their school. Today was the day! They were going on their first field trip away from school.

Soon the yellow school bus pulled up. All the little ants climbed on board. After a long and bumpy ride, the ants arrived at a farm.

Everyone, where does this story take place? (at a farm)

Hector was the first little ant off the bus. Hector smiled and took a breath of the fresh country air.

Everyone, take a big breath.

Hector, who loved the sounds of the farm, said,
"I hear 'mooooo.' What could it be?"

Everyone, what do you think Hector heard? (a cow)

Hector said,
"Oh wow! I hear a . . . cow."

Angelina was the next one off the bus.

Angelina, who loved the sounds of the farm, said,

"I hear 'neighhh.' What could it be?"

What do you think Angelina heard? (a horse)

Angelina said,
"Oh, of course, I hear a . . . horse."

Eaton was the next one off the bus.

Eaton, who loved the sounds of the farm, said,

"I hear 'bzzzz.' What could it be?"

What do you think Eaton heard? (a bee, a fly)

Eaton said,
"Oh my, I hear a . . . fly!"

Jamal was the next one off the bus.

Jamal, who loved the sounds of the farm, said,

"I hear 'meowww.' What could it be?"

What do you think Jamal heard?   (a cat)

Then Jamal, who was allergic to cats, said,

"Oh drat!

I hear a . . . cat."

Mrs. B clapped her hands. "What a smart class I have! We are going to have a wonderful day at the farm."

Mrs. B's class is having a great field trip.
Raise your hand if you've ever visited a farm.

PROCEED TO *THE BARNYARD RHYME.*

The Barnyard Rhyme

I hear "mooooo." What could it be?

Oh wow! I hear a . . . cow.

I hear "neighhh." What could it be?

Oh, of course! I hear a . . . horse.

I hear "bzzzz." What could it be?

Oh my! I hear a . . . fly.

I hear "meowww." What could it be?

Oh drat! I hear a . . . cat.

END OF CHAPTER 1

See the unit teacher's guide for the related activity: Bookmaking.

The Field Trip

CHAPTER 2 INTRODUCTION

In Chapter 1, we read about Mrs. B and the little ants on a field trip.
Does anyone remember where they are? (at a farm)
In this chapter, you will get to play an action game with Mrs. B and her class.

Chapter 2
Mrs. B's Action Game

Mrs. B and the little ants were having a great day at the farm.

After their picnic lunch, they decided to play an action game.

Mrs. B said, "I hear 'mooo.' If you think it's a cow, stand up and take a bow."

All the little ants stood up and took a bow.

Everyone, stand up and take a bow.

58

Then Mrs. B said, "I hear 'baaa.' If you think it's a sheep, pretend to be asleep."

Everyone, pretend you're asleep.

Mrs. B said, "I hear 'caw.' If you think it's a crow, bend down and touch your toe."

Everyone, touch your toe.

Mrs. B said, "I hear 'maaa.' If you think it's a goat, pretend to row a boat."

Everyone, pretend to row a boat.

Mrs. B said, "I hear 'oink.' If you think it's a pig, dance a little jig."

Everyone, dance a jig.

Mrs. B said, "That was so much fun, I think I'll write it down!"

PROCEED TO *MRS. B'S ACTION RHYME.*

Let's act out *Mrs. B's Action Rhyme.*

Mrs. B's Action Rhyme

I hear "mooo." What could it be?

I hear a cow. Stand up and take a . . . bow.

I hear "baaa." What could it be?

I hear a sheep. Pretend to be . . . asleep.

I hear "caw." What could it be?

I hear a crow. Bend down and touch your . . . toe.

I hear "maaa." What could it be?

I hear a goat. Pretend to row a . . . boat.

I hear "oink." What could it be?

I hear a pig. Dance a little . . . jig.

END OF STORY

See the unit teacher's guide for the related activity: Bookmaking.

Mrs. B is a teacher at the Ant School in the *Read Well K* stories. She is featured throughout the program and is also the acronym for the author of many of the stories in *Read Well K*. When program authors found that shared story writing allowed them to combine their talents, Mrs. B was the designated author. Mrs. B stands for Marilyn, Richard, Shelley, and Barbara.

M is for Marilyn Sprick.

Marilyn Maeda Sprick is a third generation Japanese American. She and her husband, Randy, have two grown children. They live in the woods near Eugene, Oregon, with their two dogs. Marilyn has always loved writing and art, but most of all, she loves teaching children of all ages how to read well.

R is for Richard Dunn.

Richard Dunn is a kindergarten teacher in Seattle, Washington. He lives with his wife, their two children, and a big white cat. During his free time, Richard loves to play with his children, read, and spend time outdoors hiking and camping.

S is for Shelley V. Jones.

Shelley V. Jones teaches in Oregon and lives with her husband, Lee, and a beagle named Macintosh. She is a mom with two grown kids. Shelley loves books and music and has spent her life teaching reading and music to people of all ages.

B is for Barbara Gunn.

Barbara Gunn grew up in California, where she spent her summers swimming, bike riding, and making up stories. Now she lives in Eugene, Oregon, with her husband, Steve, and two cats, Oreo and Tillie. Barbara has two grown children. She still likes making up stories and especially enjoys researching how to teach children to read well.

Philip A. Weber Jr. is the illustrator of all the Mrs. B stories and graphics. He was born and raised in Dallas, Texas. Philip began drawing as soon as he could hold a pencil. He has lots of interests, including cooking, drawing, and collecting comic books. He is also a character voice actor and loves puppetry and skiing. He now lives in Michigan with his wife, Linda; their two little girls, Brooke and Madison; and their cat, Maddie.

Chuck Marier colorized all of the Mrs. B stories. He graduated from the University of Oregon with a degree in Sequential Art. He works as a graphic designer and illustrator and publishes his own comic book about a funny superhero and his friends. Chuck lives in Eugene, Oregon, with his wife, two cats, two turtles, and several super-intelligent goldfish.